First published in Great Britain in 1980 by
Octopus Books Ltd

This edition published in 1984 by
Treasure Press
59 Grosvenor Street
London W1

© 1980 Octopus Books Ltd

ISBN 0 907812 84 8

Printed in Hong Kong

Educational and Series advisor Felicia Law

MY FIRST
ABC
BOOK

illustrated by
Peter Woolcock

TREASURE PRESS

aA

armadillos acting

b B

bears bathing

cC

cats crying

dD

dogs driving

e E

elephants eating

fF

foxes flying

g G

goats gardening

hH

hippos hurrying

Ii

iguanas invading

j J jaguars jogging

k K kangaroos kicking

l L

lions laughing

m M

monkeys
making mischief

nN nightingales nursing

oO ostriches ogling

pP

penguins parading

q Q quails quivering

r R rabbits running

s S

squirrels storing

Tt

tigers tobogganing

u U unicorns in uniform

v V voles visiting

w W

walruses washing

xX excited oxen

yY yaks yelling

zZ zebra zig-zagging